HANUMAN

The Mighty God

OM

Om Books International

High up in the heaven, Lord Brahma was meditating on his lotus throne. When he opened his eyes, he saw a beautiful young girl looking after him. He thought to himself, "She is indeed hard working. It is time I granted her a boon as a reward for her devotion." Brahma called out to the girl and said, "Oh beautiful one! I grant you a boon for your dedication at work. Ask me what you wish for!"

The girl replied, "Lord Brahma, I am under a terrible curse." When Brahma asked her what it was, she said, "When I was a child, I went to Earth to see what it was like. There I saw a strange sight. A monkey sat deep in

meditation! I was a naughty child and so threw stones at him. Alas! That was a sage in the form of a monkey. I had unknowingly disturbed him. He opened his eyes in anger

and cursed me that I would turn into a monkey the day I fall in love."

"Oh Lord! Only you can rid me of that curse," pleaded the girl. Lord Brahma fell into deep thought as he could not rid her of the

curse completely. "There is a way out of the curse, but you have to be patient," said Brahma. "A form of Lord Vishnu is to be born on Earth very soon. I now bless you that the form will be born through you and you will

be free from the curse the day you give birth to that child. The time has now come for you to leave the heavens and live on Earth."

And that is how Anjana, the mother of Hanuman, came to Earth. She lived in a forest

as a hunter and killed fearful beasts. One day, while she was hunting, she saw a handsome man fighting with a lion. She fell in love the moment she saw him, and could feel her face changing into that of a monkey. "The curse

is taking effect!" panicked Anjana. She let out a scream and fell to the ground.

The man rushed to her thinking he had scared her. Anjana was too scared to show him her face, and so she just peeped through the gaps of her fingers to see what he was

like. And she was in for a happy surprise! "He has a monkey's face too!" thought Anjana. "I am Kesari, the king of monkeys," said the young man. "Oh lovely maiden! Will you marry me?" Anjana was still in shock. But she agreed

right away. Kesari and Anjana were married with the blessings of all their elders.

While Anjana and Kesari roamed the forests in their lovely chariot, in another part of the world, King Dasharatha—the ruler of Ayodhya—was performing a holy sacrifice to have children. Agni, the God of fire, came out of the holy fire with a bowl filled with a sweet for the three queens of Dasharatha. "Dasharatha, give your three queens a portion

of this sweet and you will soon be blessed with strong and intelligent sons," said Agni. Dasharatha obeyed Agni and gave the sweet to his queens. When he had finished giving the sweet to his third wife, a kite flew in suddenly. It snatched the bowl from Dasharatha's hands and flew up into the sky.

It carried the bowl right into the open arms of Anjana, who was worshipping in the forest.

Anjana was surprised to see a bowl in her hands. She wondered, "What is this? It looks like a blessing from God himself." And so, she ate the sweet, thanking God. A few months later,

Anjana gave birth to a lovely baby, who was named Anjaneya—the son of Anjana.

Anjaneya grew up to be a chubby child. He would always be found smiling. But Anjaneya was restless like all children. One day, he was

very hungry and looked around everywhere for his mother. "Mother! I am hungry!" shouted Anjaneya. But Anjana was not to be found anywhere. Anjaneya was standing by the window at that time. He looked out of the window, tired of looking for his mother. Up in the sky he saw something that looked a red apple, waiting to be plucked. "Oh! That looks delicious," thought Anjaneya. "There is a red apple waiting to be plucked. I will go

and get it," thought Anjaneya and leapt into the sky. What he did not know was the red apple was actually the Sun!

Anjaneya flew like the wind into the skies. Right at the time when he was flying to get

the Sun, Rahu—the Snake God—was going to cover the Sun God. Anjaneya caught Rahu and refused to leave him for some time. Rahu was almost choked with Anjaneya's tight clasp, when he was suddenly released. Frightened,

Rahu ran to Indra, the king of all the gods. "Indra, I have just survived from the clutches of a child with a monkey face. Though he was a child, he held me with a mighty force. I

could not even move. Who is he?" asked
Rahu.

Indra smiled and replied, "He is Anjaneya,
the son of Anjana and Kesari." Meanwhile, the
Sun God asked his charioteer, "Who is that

little boy coming towards us with such speed?"
When the charioteer told him that it was
Anjaneya and he was coming to get them, the
Sun God ran to Indra. "Save me Indra! I cannot
run away from the mighty Anjaneya."

Indra took his chariot and rode towards Anjaneya. "The ripe fruit you are flying towards is the Sun God, my child! Leave him alone," said Indra. But Anjaneya was adamant. He refused to listen. Indra thought to himself,

"How do I stop him? He will not listen and I cannot let the Sun to be captured by him. The world will suffer!" Finally, Indra picked up Vajra, his weapon, and flung it at Anjaneya to stop him from flying ahead. Indra's weapon was a very powerful one and Anjaneya came tumbling down to Earth within seconds. He lay on the grass unconscious. Vayu, God of Winds, saw this and ran to Anjaneya's help. Seeing him speechless and unconscious, Vayu

was angry with all the gods for hurting such a young child. "As this child suffers, let the world suffer! I will take back all the air from this earth and go away," cried out Vayu. He

took Anjaneya and went deep into the
chambers of mother Earth.

All the three worlds were now without air.
People could not breathe. The gods were
choked. There was panic everywhere. Finally,
everyone ran to Indra, pleading with him to
save them. "Save us from this hell, or soon

we will all die!" cried the gods. The Sun God cursed himself for what had happened. "It was me who ran for help to Indra," said the Sun God to Lord Brahma. Brahma heard everyone's pleas and told Indra, "You must apologise to

32

Vayu. Beg him to come back or soon everything will perish."

Indra immediately rode to where Vayu was and said, "Vayu, please accept my apologies and return." Both Brahma and Indra blessed Hanuman

with great powers. "You took the force of my weapon on your cheeks (Hanu in Sanskrit) and will be known from now on as Hanuman."

Anjaneya grew up to be a very curious child. He would peep into the nests of birds to see their little children. "Look how cute these fledglings are," Anjaneya would say, looking at the nest of sparrows.

He would run around forests with his other friends saying, "Come with me! Don't be afraid!"

Anjaneya was fearless, but was very naughty. He would often trouble the sages living in the forests. "Look! Little Anjaneya took my sacred pot away," said one sage. "Oh! He always takes my sacred beads away," said another. "We have to stop this little child from wrecking our lives," said another sage. But no one could stop Anjaneya! He was as swift as the wind.

One day, Anjaneya was being his naughty self, and ran away with a basket of flowers a sage had collected for his prayers. The sage could take it no longer. He cursed Anjaneya in his anger, "You will forget all the powers you have."

Anjaneya could not believe his ears. "What will I tell my parents now!" trembled the little one. He begged the sage for forgiveness with tears in his eyes. The sage was moved by Anjaneya, and decided to give him a way out of the curse, as a curse once given can never be taken back. "You will remember your powers at the right time, when someone reminds you of them," said the sage.

Hanuman grew up to be handsome and strong. He was the Minister in the court of

Sugreev, the king of monkeys. Sugreev's brother, Bali, had banished him from the kingdom. So, Sugreev with his trusted followers, was living in the forest.

Far away in Ayodhya, Ram was sent to exile for fourteen years. He had come to live in the forest with his brother Lakshman and Sita. But evil Ravan had kidnapped Sita. Ram and Lakshman had set out to find Sita. News reached the

ears of Sugreev that two young men were entering their part of the forest. Sugreev was anxious. "Could these men have been sent by my brother Bali?" he wondered. He called Hanuman and said, "Hanuman! You are the only one who can find out who these men are and tell me whether they are friends or foes." Hanuman set out to meet Ram and Lakshman disguised as an old man. "What are you looking for, young men?" asked Hanuman when he spotted Ram and Lakshman.

"We are Ram and Lakshman, princes of Ayodhya. My wife was kidnapped by Ravan. We are on a mission to rescue her," said Ram. "Then come with me," said Hanuman assuming his real form. He took

them to Sugreev and told him all about them and Sita. Sugreev promised to help Ram, but also asked for his help in getting back his kingdom and family.

Ram helped Sugreev in defeating Bali, and crowned him King. Within a few days, Sugreev

sent out small teams in different directions to find Sita. Hanuman, Jambavan—the Bear King—and a team of monkeys went south. After touring every part of the south, the

team reached the southern-most tip, where all they could see was the sea. "What will we do now? We don't know whether Sita was taken beyond the sea!" said one of the monkeys.

"I know where she was taken," said an old voice. Everyone turned to find an old vulture

walking towards them. "I am Sampati, the brother of Jatayu," said the bird.

"Your brave brother was killed by the evil Ravan, while he was trying to rescue Sita," said Jambavan. "I did not know this," cried

out Sampati. "I will avenge my brother's death by telling you where Ravan lives. There! Across the sea live Ravan and his evil forces," said Sampati.

"But who will go across the sea?" thought Jambavan. Then he looked at Hanuman. "If

there is anyone among us who has the power to cross the sea, it is you!" said Jambavan to Hanuman. "Me? How can I cross such a big sea?" asked Hanuman. "You have great powers

waiting to be remembered! Think of Lord Ram and you will get your powers back," said Jambavan. Hanuman stood on top of a rock and meditated upon Lord Ram. Slowly he started growing in size. The monkeys watched as Hanuman grew as high as the sky!

Then he took one giant leap and flew across the sea. When he had flown a few miles, Hanuman suddenly hit a giant mountain, which had emerged from the waters, with his chest. "I am Mainaka! Your father had helped me once. I would like to repay that help by

offering you a place to rest for a while on your long journey." "I do not have the time to rest," said Hanuman and flew ahead. A little ahead, Hanuman saw a huge demoness come out of the waters. It was Sinhika. "You have to enter my mouth, if you have to go ahead," said Sinhika. "So be it!" said Hanuman, and suddenly shrunk himself as small as a fly. He entered Sinhika's mouth swiftly and flew out of it before she realised.

But troubles had not ended for Hanuman. Surasa, a demon in the form of a huge snake

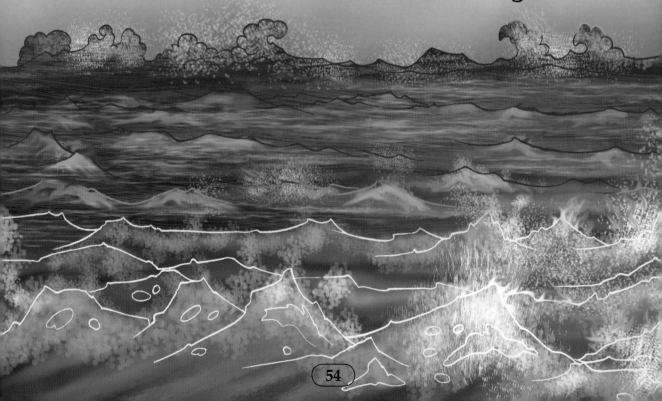

came out of the waters. She swallowed Hanuman. But being strong, Hanuman tore her stomach and came out of it within minutes. He continued his flight till he reached the gates of Lanka at night. Hanuman saw a demoness guarding the gates. He walked towards

the gates quietly, but the demoness heard his footsteps and said, "Stop! Who goes there? You have to defeat Lankini to go ahead!" Hanuman defeated Lankini in a fight but did not kill her as she was a woman.

Then he entered Lanka and went from one place to the other till he finally reached Ravan's palace. He saw many beautiful women sleeping there but not Sita. After roaming around a little more, he reached the tree top of the garden where Ravan had kept Sita.

Hanuman could clearly see Sita surrounded by demonesses. As he planned to approach her, he heard the sound of footsteps. He saw

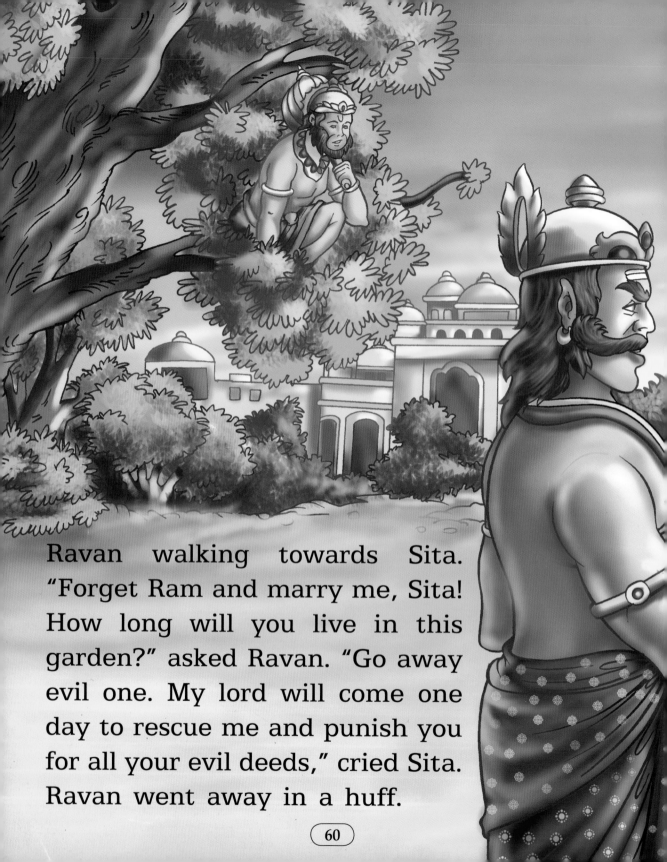

Ravan walking towards Sita. "Forget Ram and marry me, Sita! How long will you live in this garden?" asked Ravan. "Go away evil one. My lord will come one day to rescue me and punish you for all your evil deeds," cried Sita. Ravan went away in a huff.

A little later, when all the demonesses had slept, Hanuman dropped Ram's ring in Sita's lap. "My Lord! He is here!" exclaimed Sita with joy. Hanuman slowly came down the tree and said, "Mother! Your worries are over. Lord

Ram is on his way here and will defeat the evil Ravan and take you home."

Then Hanuman fought a few of the demons guarding the garden and allowed himself to be captured, so as to get a chance to be taken before Ravan. When Ravan did not offer a seat to him, Hanuman created one by growing his tail and swirling it in circles to create a throne higher than that of Ravan. "Who are you, monkey?" asked Ravan

angrily. "I am Lord Ram's humble servant. I have come to warn you that if you don't release Sita immediately, you and your kingdom will have to pay a heavy price," said Hanuman. "Take him away and set fire to his

tail," ordered Ravan. But clever Hanuman set fire to the whole of Lanka by jumping from one house to the other. After causing enough damage to Lanka, he flew back to Lord Ram. "I found Sita!" said Hanuman to Ram. He then

told Ram about the sad condition in which Sita lived.

Ram's army built a bridge of stones over the sea with the help of the Sea God and marched into Lanka. A fierce battle took place

between both sides. Indrajit, the son of Ravan, injured Lakshman severely. Lakshman was unconscious and only the Sanjeevani herb from a mountain in the Himalayas could save him. But that had to be brought back before dawn the next day. Hanuman saw Ram's plight and took off for the Himalayas. When he reached the Himalayas, Hanuman was wonderstruck. "I was told that Sanjeevani would twinkle in

the dark. But all these other herbs are also twinkling. Which one do I carry?" wondered Hanuman. With no time to waste, he uprooted the entire mountain and carried it on his palm back to Lanka. Thus, Hanuman saved Lakshman's life with his strength and special powers.

Ram finally killed Ravan in the battle and rescued Sita. He crowned Vibhishan, Ravan's brother as the next king of Lanka.

Ram, Lakshman and Sita flew back with Hanuman and Sugreev to Ayodhya. After Ram was crowned as the

King of Ayodhya, he decided to give gifts to everyone who had helped him in rescuing Sita. When it came to Hanuman, "Allow me!" said Sita. She gave her special pearl necklace to Hanuman. But he pulled out each pearl and

inspected it. All the courtiers were shocked to see Hanuman disrespecting Sita's gift. But Hanuman said, "I was only seeing whether my Lord Ram was there in these pearls.

Otherwise, this necklace has no meaning for me." Such was Hanuman's love for Ram!

When one morning Hanuman saw Sita putting sindur (vermilion) on her forehead, he asked her, "Mother, why do you do this

everyday?" "It is for the good health of Lord Ram," replied Sita. "If that is so, then I will smear sindur all over my body," said Hanuman. From that day on, Hanuman applied sindur to his entire body.

While in court with Ram and Sita one day, Hanuman heard one of the courtiers whispering, "Why is Lord Ram so partial to Hanuman? He has so many more devotees." Hanuman tore his chest in answer to this, and everyone was surprised to see Lord Ram and Sita in Hanuman's heart! Hanuman's devotion to Ram was beyond anyone's imagination.

It is said, to this day, that when one says the word Ram in prayer, Hanuman appears in an invisible form and stays on to listen to his Lord's prayer.

Brave Hanuman will remain in our prayers as the greatest example of strength, devotion, loyalty and humility.